## Beloved

Finding Happiness in Marriage

# COUPLE'S GUIDE
# – MARRIAGE ENRICHMENT

Edward Sri
Lucas Pollice
*General Editors*

AUGUSTINE INSTITUTE

Nihil obstat: Derek Barr, Censor Deputatus
Imprimatur: Most Reverend Samuel J. Aquila, S.T.L., Archbishop of Denver
January 2015

Writers: Lucas Pollice, Randy Southern, Edward Sri
Media: Steve Flanigan, Jon Ervin, Justin Leddick, Kevin Mallory, Ted Mast, John Schmidt
Print Production/Graphic Design: Justin Deister, Ann Diaz, Brenda Kraft, Jane Meyers, Devin Schadt

ACKNOWLEDGMENTS

**OurSundayVisitor**

Production of this project was made possible with the generous support of the Our Sunday Visitor Institute.

Augustine Institute
6160 South Syracuse Way, Suite 310
Greenwood Village, CO 80111
Information: 303-937-4420
AugustineInstitute.org
SymbolonCatholic.org

Printed in the United States of America
ISBN 978-0-9862288-5-8

Beloved

Finding Happiness in Marriage

# TABLE OF CONTENTS

## The Mystery and Meaning of Marriage

## Living Marriage

# BELOVED: AN INTRODUCTION

**Welcome to the *Beloved* program.** These sessions have been carefully designed to help you more deeply explore and reaffirm your role in one of God's most cherished institutions. This will be a grace-filled opportunity to enrich your marriage and to grow even closer to God and to your spouse.

You will trace God's plan for marriage, from his creation of Adam and Eve to the coming of Christ, and find your unique and vital niche within that plan. You will revisit God's plan for what it means for two to become one—a singular entity charged with mirroring God's love for his people and demonstrating his grace to the world.

You will also have the opportunity to tackle the most pressing concerns of marriage, from dealing with conflict to fostering intimacy. Using the tools of Scripture and Church teaching, you will be able to continue to forge for yourselves a sturdy, Christ-centered relationship, designed to weather life's storms and to draw each other deeper into God's love.

**How the *Beloved* Program Works**

The *Beloved* program is divided into two parts: *The Mystery and Meaning of Marriage* and *Living Marriage*.

- The Mystery and Meaning of Marriage (6 sessions) takes a "big picture" approach to the subject and provides the theological foundations for the Sacrament of Marriage as revealed in Salvation History. These sessions engage the current cultural worldview that challenges the value of marriage and help couples to understand the bond as God intended.
- Living Marriage (6 sessions) addresses specific challenges that marriage presents and provides the life skills necessary for a healthy and holy marriage, including keeping Christ at the center of the relationship, healing past wounds, and understanding God's plan for physical intimacy.

The two parts may be used individually as 6-session studies or combined to create a more comprehensive 12-session program.

**What You'll Find in Each *Beloved* Session**

**1. Introduction:** The introduction highlights the main points of the session, giving you a clear sense of what you'll be hearing about and discussing.

**2. Opening Prayer:** Each session opens with a prayer asking God to bless your time together and guide you as you turn to God to continue to strengthen your marriage relationship.

**3. Video:** Each *Beloved* video episode presents the subject matter through Sacred Scripture and Sacred Tradition of the Catholic Church along with honest and compelling stories and testimonials from married couples—the joys, struggles, and triumphs that are a part of the Sacrament of Matrimony.

**4. Small Group Discussion:** Following the video presentation, you'll discuss questions and mull over the main points of the session—and their implications for daily life—with a few other couples.

**5. Couple Discussion:** You'll have time to personalize the topic for you and your spouse; the two of you can privately discuss open-ended questions designed to help you find your own real-life application of the material.

**6. Closing Prayer:** With your leader and the other couples, close in prayer and reflect back to God an appropriate response to his loving action in the session.

**7. Couple's Activity:** A take-home activity encourages you to find specific and personalized application for the principles covered in the session.

**8. Your Journal Thoughts:** Record your reflections on the session topic both as individuals and as a couple using the journaling space at the end of each session in your Couple's Guide.

**Practical Living**

- *A Catholic Handbook for Engaged and Newly Married Couples*—Frederick W. Marks, Ph.D. (Emmaus Road Publishing)
- *Amazing Grace for Married Couples*—Jeff Cavins, Matthew Pinto, and Patti Armstrong (Ascension Press)
- *The Five Love Languages: How to Express Heartfelt Commitment to Your Mate*—Greg Chapman (Northfield)
- *For Better...Forever: A Catholic Guide to Lifelong Marriage*—Dr. Gregory Popcak (Our Sunday Visitor)
- *Just Married: The Catholic Guide to Surviving the First Five Years of Marriage*—Dr. Greg and Lisa Popcak (Ave Maria Press)
- *Life-Giving Love: Embracing God's Beautiful Design for Marriage*—Kimberly Hahn (St. Anthony Messenger Press)
- *Love in the Little Things: Tales of Family Life*—Mike Aquilina (St. Anthony Messenger Press)
- *Marriage 911: How God Saved Our Marriage (and Can Save Yours, Too!)*—Greg and Julie Alexander (Servant Books)
- *Marriage: Small Steps, Big Rewards*—Dr. Ray Guarendi (Servant Books)
- *Married Saints and Blesseds Through the Centuries*—Ferdinand Holbock (Ignatius Press)
- *Men and Women Are From Eden*—Mary Healy (Servant Books)
- *Men, Women, and the Mystery of Love: Practical Insights from John Paul II's Love and Responsibility*—Dr. Edward Sri (Servant Books)
- *Three to Get Married*—Archbishop Fulton Sheen (Scepter Publishers, Inc.)
- *What God Has Joined: A Catholic Teaching on Marriage*—Most Rev. Kevin W. Vann (Basilica Press)

**Theology of Marriage**

- *Catholic for a Reason IV: Scripture and the Mystery of Marriage and Family Life*—Scott Hahn and Regis J. Flaherty (Emmaus Road Publishing)
- *Good News About Sex and Marriage: Answers to Your Honest Questions About Catholic Teaching*—Christopher West (Servant Books)
- *Love and Responsibility*—Karol Wojtyla (Pope John Paul II) (Pauline Books & Media)
- *Marriage: The Rock on Which the Family Is Built*—William May (Ignatius Press)
- *What God Has Joined…The Sacramentality of Marriage*—Peter J. Elliot (Wipf and Stock Publishers)

**Magisterial Teaching**  (All available through the Vatican website—vatican.va)
- On Christian Marriage *(Casti Connubii)*—Pope Pius XI
- On the Regulation of Birth *(Humanae Vitae)*—Pope Paul VI
- On the Family *(Familiaris Consortio)*—Pope John Paul II
- *Preparation for the Sacrament of Marriage*—The Pontifical Council for the Family
- *The Truth and Meaning of Human Sexuality*—The Pontifical Council for the Family
- *Letter to Families*—Pope John Paul II
- *The Catechism of the Catholic Church*:
  - ➤ The Sacrament of Matrimony: 1601–1666
  - ➤ Sexual Ethics: 2331-2400; 2514–2533
  - ➤ The Christian Family: 2196–2233
- *The United States Catholic Catechism for Adults*:
  - ➤ The Sacrament of Marriage: Chapter 21
  - ➤ The Christian Family: Chapter 28
  - ➤ Sexual Ethics: Chapters 30 and 33

**Marriage and Family Apostolates**
- Alexander House Apostolate: thealexanderhouse.org
- Retrouvaille: retrouvaille.org
- World Wide Marriage Encounter: wwme.org
- Catholic Engaged Encounter: engagedencounter.org
- The Apostolate for Family Consecration: afc.org
- Chastity Project: chastityproject.org
- For Your Marriage (USCCB): foryourmarriage.org
- Theology of the Body Institute: tobinstitute.org

## *A Prayer of Husband and Wife*

O God, we want to live our life together with you and always to continue it with you. Help us never to hurt and never to grieve each other. Help us to share all our works, all our hopes, all our dreams, all our successes, all our failures, all our joys and all our sorrows. Help us to have no secrets from each other so that we may be truly one. Keep us always true to each other, and grant that all the years ahead may draw us ever closer to each other. Grant that nothing may ever come between us and nothing may ever make us drift apart. And as we live with each other, help us to live with you, so that our love may grow perfect in your love, for you are the God whose name is love. This we ask for your love's sake. Amen.

# SESSION 1

## DOES MARRIAGE MATTER?

## DOES MARRIAGE MATTER?

## INTRODUCTION

Long before governments and societies ever discussed marriage, God put on the human heart a longing for the unique life-long commitment and total self-giving love found in the sacrament of Matrimony. We're going to see how marriage corresponds to this human desire for a lasting love, and how it's also good for our happiness and good for a flourishing society.

But even more than that, we're going to see that underneath this ancient institution known as marriage, there's something much deeper at work. Marriage is bound up with God's plan for the entire world. In our marriages we participate in something much greater than our human affection for each other or the wonderful desire to be with the one we love. We are caught up into something so much bigger than our own human love. We are caught up into God's love.

## OPENING PRAYER

***Pray together the following prayer:***

Heavenly Father,

Through the intercession of the Holy Family, help us treasure the gift of marriage that reflects the love of Christ for the Church, where the self-giving love of husband and wife unites them more perfectly and cooperates in your plan for new life created in your image.

Help us support men and women in their vocation of marriage, especially in difficult times when they join their sufferings to the Cross. Help us uphold the institution of marriage in our society as the place where love is nurtured and family life begins. Help us acknowledge that our future depends on this love and your providential care for us.

Amen.

*"Marriage based on exclusive and definitive love becomes the icon of the relationship between God and his people and vice versa."*
—Pope Benedict XVI, Encyclical *Deus Caritas Est*, n. 11, 2005

# SMALL GROUP DISCUSSION

**1. If we are hardwired to desire the faithful, permanent, and exclusive love of marriage, why is marriage so difficult sometimes?**

_____

_____

**2. Imagine that you're having lunch with a single friend who claims that marriage is overrated and then challenges you to prove otherwise. What would you say in response?**

_____

_____

*"Today, there are those who say that marriage is out of fashion... They say that it is not worth making a lifelong commitment, making a definitive decision, 'forever,' because we do not know what tomorrow will bring. I ask you, instead, to be revolutionaries, I ask you to swim against the tide; yes, I am asking you to rebel against this culture that sees everything as temporary and that ultimately believes you are incapable of responsibility, that believes you are incapable of true love."*
—Pope Francis, World Youth Day on July 28, 2013

# COUPLE'S DISCUSSON

**1. What preconceived notions—perhaps unrealistic hopes and expectations—about marriage did each of you have before you got married?**

_____

_____

**2. What challenges or problems did your preconceived notions about marriage create?**

_____

_____

*"Therefore a man leaves his father and his mother and cleaves to his wife, and they become one flesh."* —Genesis 2:24

*Photo Credit: Wedding rings © J.Schelkle/ Shutterstock.com*

11

## CLOSING PRAYER

*Pray together the following prayer:*

Almighty God,

We aspire to the ideal of marriage that you established long before any other cultural or governmental statutes existed. Your Holy Scriptures say, "God made them male and female"; "For this reason a man shall leave his father and mother and be joined to his wife, and the two shall become one"; "So they are no longer two but one. What therefore God has joined together, let not man put asunder."

Bless our efforts to protect and nourish the union you have ordained.

Amen.

## COUPLE'S ACTIVITY

You saw in the video how our marriages are caught up into God's plan for the entire world and how in the Sacrament of Matrimony our human love participates in God's very love for us. This will be explored more in the next several sessions. But for now, take some time to step back and ponder, "What is God's plan for marriage?" Some key aspects of this plan can be found in the *Catechism of the Catholic Church,* 1601-1605.

If you do not have a Catechism, there is an online version that you can find at: www.usccb.org/beliefs-and-teachings/what-we-believe/catechism/

Take some time this week to read these paragraphs in the *Catechism* and really ponder the truths about marriage that God's plan reveals.

_____

_____

Then, discuss with each other how this plan affects how each of you views your marriage, and perhaps how you live out your marriage on a daily basis. Perhaps it helps you have a deeper appreciation for your marriage and your spouse, or gives you greater comfort in your marriage. It may also reveal some ways in which you have not been living your marriage as God desires. In any case, this is the beginning of this journey together to discover more deeply God's plan for your marriage.

Consider starting a marriage journal to record passages that have special meaning to you and your spouse.

# Your Journal Thoughts

_____

_____

_____

_____

_____

_____

_____

_____

_____

_____

_____

_____

_____

_____

_____

_____

_____

_____

# Your Journal Thoughts

# SESSION 2

## ENTERING THE STORY OF MARRIAGE

# SESSION 2

## ENTERING THE STORY OF MARRIAGE

### INTRODUCTION

The creation of Eve from Adam's side represents the pinnacle of God's creative work because it reveals the marital love between Adam and Eve, which, in a profound way, represents God's love for the world. The sin they commit, however, ruptures their love—for one another and for God. God does not allow the relationship to remain ruptured, but by assuming the role of the Bridegroom, he establishes an intimate covenant with his people. Jesus becomes human to save us *from* sin—and *for* a love that lasts forever. That is the love story we become a part of in a new way when we marry.

### OPENING PRAYER

**Pray together the following prayer:**

Almighty God,

We love you and are grateful that we can come before you, knowing that you accept us as your children whom you love. Take ownership of us, guide us, prompt us, teach us, and instruct us, dear God, in the way we should go. May your great plan for our lives be fulfilled so that we may be closer to you.

Amen.

*"And I will betroth you to me for ever. I will betroth you to me in righteousness and in justice, in steadfast love and in mercy."*　　　　—Hosea 2:19

# SMALL GROUP DISCUSSION

**1. What does it mean to be made in the image of God, the Holy Trinity? What implications does this have for the way we live each day?**

_____

_____

**2. Describe the kind of unity and trust Adam and Eve experienced in their marriage relationship.**

_____

_____

**3. We saw how, after sin first entered their hearts, Adam and Eve no longer experienced total trust and security in their marriage relationship. What are some of the fears that keep a husband or wife from being closer to their spouse? What fears keep spouses from letting their beloved know what's really on their hearts or seeing them as they really are?**

_____

_____

> *"Being a person in the image and likeness of God thus also involves existing in a relationship, in relation to the other 'I'."*
> —St. John Paul II, *Mulieris Dignitatem*, #7

# COUPLE'S DISCUSSION

**1. We learned how Adam and Eve saw each other as a tremendous gift from God. Take a few minutes to quietly reflect on ways in which your spouse is a gift to you. Then share your reflections with your spouse.**

_____

_____

**2. Ask each other, "What is one thing I can do to build greater trust and unity in our marriage?" Be completely open to what your spouse has to say.**

_____

_____

*Photo Credit: Sistine Chapel, The Creation of Adam © AISA – Everett/Shutterstock.com*

**3. Resolve to put that one recommendation from your spouse into practice this upcoming week.**

_____

_____

> *"...forbearing one another and, if one has a complaint against another, forgiving each other; as the Lord has forgiven you, so you also must forgive. And above all these put on love, which binds everything together in perfect unity. And let the peace of Christ rule in your hearts, to which indeed you were called in the one body. And be thankful."*
> —Colossians 3:13-15

## CLOSING PRAYER

**_Pray together the following marriage blessing prayer:_**

We thank you, O God, for the love you have implanted in our hearts. May it always inspire us to be kind in our words, considerate of feeling, and concerned for each other's needs and wishes. Help us to be understanding and forgiving of human weaknesses and failings. Increase our faith and trust in you, and may your prudence guide our life and love. Bless our marriage, O God, with peace and happiness, and make our love fruitful for your glory and our joy both here and in eternity.

Amen.

## COUPLE'S ACTIVITY

At the end of Session 2, you reflected on ways that your spouse is a gift to you. In the discussion that followed, your spouse shared with you one thing you could do to build greater trust and unity in your relationship.

Your task this week is to honor that request to the best of your ability. For example, let's say your spouse requested that the two of you talk more in the evening. You might honor that request by...

- keeping a mini-diary of conversation-worthy things that happen during the day;
- spending more time reading newspapers or watching the news so that you have topics to talk about; or
- brainstorming questions to ask your spouse.

At the end of the week, ask your spouse for feedback on your efforts, and then make the necessary adjustments.

*Photo Credit: The Holy Trinity / Gianni Dagli Orti / The Art Archive at Art Resource, NY*

# *Your Journal Thoughts*

_____

_____

_____

_____

_____

_____

_____

_____

_____

_____

_____

_____

_____

_____

_____

_____

_____

_____

# *Your Journal Thoughts*

_____

_____

_____

_____

_____

_____

_____

_____

_____

_____

_____

_____

_____

_____

_____

_____

_____

# SESSION 3

## LOVE REVEALED

The Mystery and Meaning of Marriage

Beloved

# SESSION 3

## LOVE REVEALED

### INTRODUCTION

Marriage is more than a union between a husband and wife; it is also a sacrament—an external sign, instituted by Christ, that imparts God's transforming grace. The vows of the marriage sacrament are profoundly important because it is the covenant of love expressed in the vows between the husband and wife that becomes a real, living sign of Christ's love for the Church. By demonstrating Christ's sacrificial, freely given, faithful, and fruitful love in your relationship with your spouse, you help others experience God's grace and presence in the world. This is why marriage matters!

### OPENING PRAYER

*Pray together the following prayer:*

We thank you, O God, the Author of love, for the wisdom, the hope, and the challenge contained in your divine Word—your incredible love story—where we find these words:

*"God shows his love for us in that while we were yet sinners Christ died for us."*
—Roman 5:8

*"Greater love has no man than this, that a man lay down his life for his friends."*
—John 15:13

*"Husbands, love your wives, as Christ loved the church and gave himself up for her."*
—Ephesians 5:25

Lord, we ask that you move in our midst during this session. Bless our efforts to better understand the Sacrament of Marriage and to become instruments of your grace.

Amen.

*"It is love that makes the human person the authentic image of the Blessed Trinity, [the] image of God."*
—Pope Benedict XVI, homily on June 3, 2012

# SMALL GROUP DISCUSSION

**1. Let's review to make sure we understand one of the main points in today's session: the relationship between the wedding vows and Christ's love for us on the cross. What are some of the things you said when you made your wedding vows? Specifically, what are the four key aspects of the vows?**

_____

_____

**• How do each of these reflect Christ's love for the Church?**

_____

_____

**2. According to Scripture, marriage is a participation in the "great mystery" of Christ's sacrificial love for us on the cross (Ephesians 5). How surprised were you at how much sacrifice marriage requires? In what ways have you as a couple grown in practicing sacrificial love?**

_____

_____

**3. The call to imitate Christ's sacrificial love is challenging. Imagine that you and your spouse are mentoring a newlywed couple. They love each other, but they're feeling the pressure of trying to live up to the ideal of Jesus' sacrificial love. What would you say to them?**

_____

_____

*"This is how all will know that you are my disciples, if you have love for one another."* —John 13:35

*Photo Credit: The Crucifixion / Scala / Art Resource, NY*

## COUPLE'S DISCUSSION

**1. The woman in the video talked about how training for a marathon together helped her and her husband-to-be prepare for marriage, because it required sacrifice and hard work and demonstrated that marriage isn't a sprint but a lifelong commitment. Each day, we're given opportunities to renew that commitment— to say "I do," in a sense, again and again in our interactions with each other.**

**Take a few minutes to think about one thing you greatly appreciate about the way your spouse treats you—a way in which you feel as honored, cherished, valued, or appreciated as you were on your wedding day. Even if your marriage has many challenges, try to think of a time when your spouse loved you like Christ loves us— or one way in which your spouse shows you a total, faithful, fruitful love. Share that with your spouse.**

_____

_____

**2. Jesus shows love for us freely, totally, faithfully, and fruitfully, and he calls us to do the same for our spouse. Of those four aspects of Jesus' love, which one presents the biggest challenge for you in your marriage? Why?**

_____

_____

> *"The family is, so to speak, the domestic church. In it parents should, by their word and example, be the first preachers of the faith to their children; they should encourage them in the vocation which is proper to each of them, fostering with special care vocation to a sacred state."* —Lumen Gentium 11

## CLOSING PRAYER

*Pray together the following prayer to the Sacred Heart of Jesus:*

O most Sacred Heart of Jesus,
King and center of all hearts,
dwell in our hearts and be our King;
grant us by your grace to love each other truly and chastely,
even as you have loved your spotless Bride, the Church,
and have given yourself up for her.

Bestow upon us that mutual love
and Christian forbearance
which are so highly acceptable in your sight,
and a mutual patience in bearing each other's defects;

for we are certain that no living creature is free from them.
Do not permit even the slightest defect to mar that full and gentle
harmony of spirit,
the foundation of the mutual assistance
in the many and varied hardships of life….

O Lord God, grant that between us there may reign a perpetual holy rivalry
toward a life perfectly Christian,
by virtue of which there may shine forth more and more clearly
the Divine image of your mystic union with your Holy Church,
as you have deigned to imprint it upon us
on the auspicious day of our being made one,
and so living, may both of us ascend into heaven,
and merit to praise you and bless you forever.

Amen.

## COUPLE'S ACTIVITY

Which aspect of Christ's love is most difficult for you to reflect? Giving love freely, totally, faithfully, or fruitfully? Your answer will set the course for your week. If, for example, you struggle with showing love faithfully, your challenge is to find seven ways to show faithful love to your spouse this week—one per day.

Put some thought into your strategy. The better you get at showing love to your spouse, in all aspects, the more clearly people will experience Christ's love through your marriage.
Here are a few ideas to get you started:

### Giving Love Freely
- Tell your spouse why you love her.
- Find a creative way to express your love that you've never tried before.

### Giving Love Totally
- Share with your spouse some of the areas in which you tend to hold back, relationally speaking. If you can explain why, share that, too.
- Think of something you can sacrifice this week in order to do something for your spouse.

### Giving Love Faithfully
- Invite your spouse to share her feelings about your friendships and acquaintances.
- Tell your spouse how you envision your future together—five years from now, ten years from now, twenty years from now and so on. Help her see that you're in it for the long haul.

### Giving Love Fruitfully
- Spend some time in prayer, asking God to align your heart with his in the matter of children.
- Make an appointment to share some of your reservations with your priest.
- Talk to some parents you respect to get their perspective on parenting.

# *Your Journal Thoughts*

_____

_____

_____

_____

_____

_____

_____

_____

_____

_____

_____

_____

_____

_____

_____

_____

_____

_____

# SESSION 4

## TOTAL GIFT OF SELF

# SESSION 4

## TOTAL GIFT OF SELF

## INTRODUCTION

Self-giving love is God's ideal for marriage. In his plan, spouses willingly surrender their personal autonomy and freedom for the sake of one another. In a real sense, marriage involves a dying to self. Such a commitment requires virtues such as generosity, patience, courage, and humility, so that spouses can seek what's best for their beloved's good and not just their own self-centered interests. Such a commitment also entails a total acceptance of the other person, even with his or her faults and weaknesses.

The most intimate expression of self-giving love is sex. Genuine sexual intimacy is unitive (a total coming together of body, soul, and emotions) and procreative (ever open to the possibility of creating new human life). If either aspect is thwarted, the act is distorted and no longer a mutual total gift of self between the spouses. As we will see, God's plan for marriage and sex is to bring about a true union between husband and wife—how God calls spouses to truly become one.

## OPENING PRAYER

***Pray together the following prayer:***

Loving Jesus, sweetness of our hearts,

Your magnetic love draws us to you. You taught us the meaning of true love by mercifully forgiving all our sins and dying on the Cross for our salvation. Teach us to embrace such divine love, that our actions be the fruits of your Spirit. Transform our souls into pure abounding love, enabling us to always walk in righteousness. Your endowment of love is priceless, being sought out by all living souls. In your mercy, inundate us with your love!

Amen.

*"A love that opens up to the other person in his unique individuality speaks the decisive words: 'I want you to be there.' Unless we begin with this acceptance of the other, however he may appear, recognizing in him a true if perhaps indistinct image of Christ, we cannot say that we truly love."*
—St. John Paul II, Cottolengo, Italy on April 13, 1980

# SMALL GROUP DISCUSSION

**1. What are some of the virtues that are needed in a marriage relationship? Which ones are the most difficult to put into practice?**

_____

_____

**2. What video talked about the temptation to treat our spouse like we do the TV—always trying to change the channels. Do you find yourself often wanting to change your spouse rather than accepting him or her? Does your desire to change your spouse actually call you to die in some way to yourself?**

_____

_____

**3. How does God's plan for sex truly bring about and protect the love and total self-giving of spouses?**

_____

_____

> "When the day of our wedding comes, I will come and take you away from them, and there will be pain – the pain of love and the pain of a new birth – and we shall be so intensely joyful and we shall stand on the border of what in human language must be called happiness."
> —Christopher, *The Jeweler's Shop*, by Karol Wojtyla (St. John Paul II)

# COUPLE'S DISCUSSION

**1. The woman in the video asked her fiancé, "What do you want?" He replied, "I want to be completely known." What are some of the ways that you do not feel completely known or completely accepted? What can each of you do to help your spouse feel more completely known and accepted?**

_____

_____

*Photo Credit: Giving flowers to his love on a winter day © Kamil Macniak/Shutterstock.com*

**2. In this session, you learned about God's plan for sexual intimacy—a total gift of self, always open to the possibility of life. Take an honest look at your sexual intimacy: Are you expressing this intimacy according to God's plan? Or has an element of selfishness, the lack of gift of self, or the use of the other entered into your sexual intimacy through contraception or other things? What can you do as a couple to foster sexual intimacy that is a total gift to one another?**

---

*"Marriage based on exclusive and definitive love becomes the icon of the relationship between God and his people and vice versa. God's way of loving becomes the measure of human love."*

—Pope Benedict XVI, *Deus Caritas Est* #11

## CLOSING PRAYER

*Pray together the following prayer:*

Jesus, fortress of mankind,

You are immaculate as God and man! Bless us with your infinite graces that we may remain in a state of purity. Strengthen us—body, spirit, and soul—to continually reflect your chastity. Protect our souls in our daily struggles, guiding us to ponder on your godliness. Defend us from the forces of evil, those that seek to acquire our souls. We are truly yours forever and ever.

Holy is our King, the Conqueror of sin!

Amen.

*Photo Credit: The Kiss / Cameraphoto Arte, Venice / Art Resource, NY*

## COUPLE'S ACTIVITY

One of the key points of the video is that marriage involves a dying to one's self. When we say, "I do," we commit to a selfless love for our spouse. We die to our old self-centered nature.

That's the plan, at least. Execution is a tricky thing.

Some habits, attitudes, and expectations die more slowly than others. Your job this week is to identify the ones that survived your wedding. Talk about the biggest challenges you face in showing each other the kind of selfless love that God calls us to.

- Perhaps the notion of *quid pro quo* is difficult for you to shake. You expect your gestures of love to be reciprocated and get frustrated or angry when they aren't.
- Perhaps you have certain very strong interests, such as gaming or shopping, that your spouse doesn't share.
- Perhaps you're the impetuous type who doesn't always consider the implications of your choices.
- Perhaps you've discovered that selflessness is a lot more difficult than you anticipated.
- Perhaps you have trouble giving yourself fully to your spouse in sexual intimacy due to a fear of pregnancy.

After you've identified the challenges, talk about why you struggle with them. For example, if you grew up in a household where fair play was emphasized, the idea of giving only as much as your spouse does makes sense to you.

Brainstorm some strategies this week to jumpstart your selflessness.

- Write reminder notes to yourself.
- Sacrifice something you really want to do for the sake of something your spouse really wants to do.
- Ask God to soften your heart and help you become more tender toward your spouse.
- Talk to a mentor couple. Solicit their advice for your situation.

With some work, you can dramatically increase your output of selfless love.

*Your Journal Thoughts*

# SESSION 5

## A SACRAMENTAL BOND

# SESSION 5

## A SACRAMENTAL BOND

## INTRODUCTION

When we are married, God forges the bond of love through his presence and his grace. Through that bond, he dwells at the center of our relationship. That is why it is sometimes said, "It takes three to get married." The covenantal bond of love in marriage is made possible by the consent of the bride and groom on the wedding day. It is then consummated on the wedding night through the total gift of self in sexual intimacy.

The Sacrament of Matrimony has three characteristics—it's fruitful (open to the creation of new life); it's exclusive (for the husband and wife alone to share); and it's indissoluble (a lifelong commitment). This covenant of love between spouses is not possible on our own, but is made possible through the Sacrament of Matrimony. Through the sacrament, a font of grace is constantly present to husband and wife to enable them to deepen their union and love each other as Christ loved the Church. Therefore, the Sacrament of Matrimony is not only a natural bond, but a supernatural one as well.

## OPENING PRAYER

***Pray together the following prayer:***

O God, who consecrated the bond of Marriage by so great a mystery that in the wedding covenant you foreshadow the Sacrament of Christ and his Church, grant, we pray, to these your servants, that what they receive in faith they may live out in deeds. Through our Lord Jesus Christ, your Son, who lives and reigns with you in the unity of the Holy Spirit, one God, for ever and ever.

Amen.

—Rite of Marriage Opening Prayer Option B, Roman Missal (2010)

*"To wed, for two Christians, is first and foremost an act of faith; it is a way to transfer their human love into the supernatural order, it is an entrusting of their love to God, so that God himself will take it into his care, guaranteeing it with his grace and his benediction."*
—St. John Paul II, from a homily at a Mass for families in 1996

# SMALL GROUP DISCUSSION

**1. In the Sacrament of Marriage, God came to dwell in the center of your relationship in such a way that he created a supernatural bond between you and your spouse. In what ways do you think God's presence has made a difference in your relationship? How can you better tap into God's grace, which is always present in your marriage?**

_____

_____

**2. What are some imperfections you've seen rise to the surface in your marriage? How can these be occasions of growing in love and holiness?**

_____

_____

**3. The video mentioned that God is with us through the rocky spots, potholes, U-turns, and misdirection in our marital journey. When was the last time you noticed God's guiding hand in your marriage?**

_____

_____

*"[Spouses] belonging to each other is the real representation, by means of the sacramental sign, of the very relationship of Christ with the Church. Spouses are therefore the permanent reminder to the Church of what happened on the Cross; they are for one another and for the children witnesses to the salvation in which the sacrament makes them sharers."*
—St. John Paul II, , *Familiaris Consortio* #13

*Photo Credit: The Marriage / Cameraphoto Arte, Venice/Art Resource, NY*

## COUPLE'S DISCUSSION

**1. One presenter described marriage as a "school of self-giving." How has your marriage challenged each of you to grow in self-giving? How might some of the messiness in marriage—personal faults, conflict, the storms of life—offer opportunities to grow in self-giving?**

_____

_____

**2. How strong is your bond of matrimony right now? How did it become that way? What can you do to continue to strengthen your bond?**

_____

_____

> *"Let the word of Christ dwell in you richly, teach and admonish one another in all wisdom, and sing psalms and hymns and spiritual songs with thankfulness in your hearts to God. And whatever you do, in word or deed, do everything in the name of the Lord Jesus, giving thanks to God the Father through him."*
> —Colossians 3:16-17

## CLOSING PRAYER

***Pray together the following prayer:***

May God the eternal Father keep you of one heart in love for one another, that the peace of Christ may dwell in you and abide always in your home.

*Response*: Amen.

May you be blessed in your children, have solace in your friends, and enjoy true peace with everyone.

*Response*: Amen.

May you be witnesses in the world to God's charity, so that the afflicted and needy who have known your kindness may one day receive you thankfully into the eternal dwelling of God.

*Response*: Amen.

—Rite of Marriage Solemn Blessing Option A, Roman Missal (2010)

*Photo Credit: Groom carrying bride near church © Artem and Victoria Popovy / Shutterstock.com*

## COUPLE'S ACTIVITY

Your challenge this week is to take some time together to think about how you can better draw upon the font of grace that is at the center of your marriage. Find a quiet place to pray together—perhaps your church or adoration chapel. Ask God how he would like to more richly bless your marriage through his presence and his grace.

During prayer, each one of you should separately write down some thoughts and ideas that come to mind. Then discuss what each of you received during your time of prayer and determine what you as a couple can do to more frequently draw upon the grace of God in your marriage.

Your ideas might include any of the following:

- Pray together each day, even for 5-10 minutes, asking God to help you love, serve, and forgive each other.

- Make a commitment to pray for one another and yourself every day to allow God to change your hearts and help overcome the challenges in your marriage.

- Go to Mass together not only on Sunday, but one other day a week.

- Go to confession together at least once a month.

- Make a commitment whenever conflicts or hurts arise in the marriage to take some time to pray and ask for God's grace to overcome the situation.

### Your Ideas?

_____

_____

_____

_____

_____

Once you have decided what you are going to do as a couple, write it down and place it in a small prayer space that you create in your home. It does not have to be anything fancy—perhaps a small table with a candle and a Bible on it, or even a crucifix and a prayer book on the bedside table. This will serve as a reminder to daily to draw upon God's grace in your marriage.

# *Your Journal Thoughts*

_____
_____
_____
_____
_____
_____
_____
_____
_____
_____
_____
_____
_____
_____
_____
_____
_____
_____

# SESSION 6

## REAL CHALLENGES, REAL LOVE

The Mystery and Meaning of Marriage

Beloved

# SESSION 6

## REAL CHALLENGES, REAL LOVE

### INTRODUCTION

The covenant for life that is the Sacrament of Matrimony encompasses…

- the blessings of marriage—being loved and made holy through the power of the Holy Spirit;
- the baggage that you bring to marriage—living out your wedding vows every day, regardless of your beloved's wounds, imperfections, or shortcomings;
- the hardships of marriage—recognizing that despite your circumstances, you are better for God together than you are individually;
- the conflict that comes with marriage—employing strategies that ultimately benefit your relationship, as opposed to trying to win arguments;
- the sexual intimacy of marriage—finding ways to promote oneness, in and out of the bedroom;
- the joys and challenges of parenting—showing your children love in meaningful ways.

### OPENING PRAYER

***Pray together the following prayer:***

Be attentive to our prayers, O Lord, and in your kindness uphold what you have established for the increase of the human race, so that the union you have created may be kept safe by your assistance.

Through our Lord Jesus Christ, your Son, who lives and reigns with you in the unity of the Holy Spirit, one God, forever and ever.

Amen.

*"Promising love for ever is possible when we perceive a plan bigger than our own ideas and undertakings, a plan which sustains us and enables us to surrender our future entirely to the one we love."*
—Pope Francis, Encyclical *Lumen Fidei*, n. 52, 2013

# SMALL GROUP DISCUSSION

**1.  Why is it important for married couples to recognize—and emphasize—that divorce is never an option, that neither one of them is "going anywhere"?**

_____

_____

**2.  One of the husbands in the video revealed an extraordinary answer to prayer he received in the midst of a conflict. In essence, God said, "It doesn't matter who's right or wrong. Love your spouse." If you took those words to heart every day, what impact would it have on your marriage?**

_____

_____

**3.  What have you learned about God's love from parenting your children?**

_____

_____

> *"The family comes from God. It is the Creator who has arranged the loving covenant of one man and one woman. He has blessed their love and made it a source of mutual help. He has made it fruitful, and established its permanence until death."*
> —St. John Paul II, Holy Mass for Families, Onitsha, Nigeria, February 13, 1982

# COUPLE'S DISCUSSION

**1.  Which story, perspective, or piece of advice in the video had the biggest impact on you?**

_____

_____

**2.  If the two of you had been part of that dinner conversation, what hard-earned wisdom would you have brought to the table? What have you experienced in your relationship that other couples could benefit from?**

_____

_____

*Photo Credit: Romantic Young Couple in Love © EpicStockMedia / Shutterstock.com*

*"Man must live on the earth, and to live there he needs not only a building constructed on a material foundation; today he needs a spiritual foundation. Love, faithfulness, and virtue in marriage constitute that foundation on which alone the matrimonial community can rest, the foundation on which the spiritual dwelling for the future family can be built."*

—St. John Paul II, the wedding ceremony
of two young Romans on February 25, 1979

## CLOSING PRAYER

### Solemn Blessing from the Rite of Marriage

May the Lord Jesus, who graced the marriage at Cana by his presence, bless you and your loved ones.

*Response*: Amen.

May he, who loved the Church to the end, unceasingly pour his love into your hearts.

*Response*: Amen.

May the Lord grant that, bearing witness to faith in his Resurrection, you may await with joy the blessed hope to come.

*Response*: Amen.

—Rite of Marriage Solemn Blessing Option C, Roman Missal (2010)

## COUPLE'S ACTIVITY

Your final activity for this study is to host a table discussion like the one depicted in the video. Invite two or more other couples to your house for coffee. Ideally one of the couples should be a little more seasoned and experienced in marriage than you are and one of the couples should be less seasoned and experienced (perhaps even newlyweds or marriage prep attendees). That way, you'll be able to give and receive mentoring advice. Older couples can also benefit from the fresh perspectives of younger couples.

If you'd prefer, you can use the six sections of the video as touchstones for your conversation. For example, you might talk about any or all of the following topics:

*Surprises*

- Why is it a good thing to be stretched by the crosses and challenges of marriage?

- Describe the security that your marriage gives you.

*Conflict*

- What's the worst mistake a couple can make when conflict arises?

- How do you resist the urge to prove that you're right or to "win a point" in the midst of a conflict?

*Our Past*

- Of the baggage you brought to your relationship, how much were you aware of before you got married and how much did you discover only after you got married?

- What does it mean to live out your wedding vows every day?

*Hardships*

- What's the most serious hardship your relationship has ever faced?

- Why is it important to have mentors or role models for your marriage?

*Sexual Intimacy*

- What are the biggest obstacles you face when it comes to physical intimacy?

- How do you work through those obstacles?

*The Blessing of Children*

- What's the most authentic expression of love you've ever received from your children?

- How does it make you feel to know that your children won't always obey you, but they'll never fail to imitate you?

There is no mandate to cover every topic. Let the conversation unfold naturally. When the discussion wanes on one subject, you can introduce another.

# *Your Journal Thoughts*

_____

_____

_____

_____

_____

_____

_____

_____

_____

_____

_____

_____

_____

_____

_____

_____

_____

_____

# SESSION 1

## CHRIST AT THE CENTER

# SESSION 1

## CHRIST AT THE CENTER

### INTRODUCTION

What is really at the center of your life *and* the center of your marriage? Only he can fulfill your deepest desires and give peace to your restless heart. If you expect your spouse (or anyone or anything else) to meet your innermost needs, you set yourself up for inevitable disappointment and disillusionment.

Jesus asks his followers, "Who do you say I am?" If he's just a good man or a wise philosopher, then it's okay to make him merely *a part of* our life. If, however, he is the Lord God, then we must welcome Jesus at the very center of our life and marriage.

### OPENING PRAYER

***Pray together the following Prayer of Spouses to the Holy Spirit:***

O Holy Spirit,
Spirit of unity, love and goodwill of Father and Son,
you have made us one in the sacred union of marriage.
Grant that, like the first Christians, we may be one heart and one mind.

Make us respect one another,
help one another in our striving for holiness,
and support one another.
Be our Guide,
our Counselor,
and our Consoler.
Make us bear one another's burdens during our journey to heaven,
where we hope to live forever as adopted children of the Triune God.

Amen.

*"Husbands, love your wives, as Christ loved the church and gave himself up for her."*　　　　　　　　　　—Ephesians 5:25

# SMALL GROUP DISCUSSION

**1. St. Augustine said, "Our hearts are restless until they rest in you." That is, our hearts are restless until Christ is the center of our lives—and our marriages. Describe a time in which you experienced a restless heart in your life or in your marriage.**

_____

_____

**2. Look at the following three diagrams. How would you describe each diagram as it pertains to priorities and who is at the center of your life?**

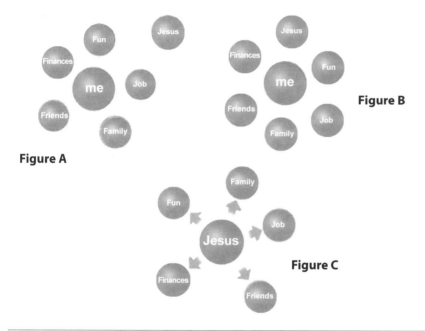

Figure A

Figure B

Figure C

**• In all honesty, which diagram most accurately reflects the way you are living out your relationship with Christ right now?**

_____

**• What can you do to put Christ more at the center of your life?**

_____

_____

*"Being Christian is not the result of an ethical choice or a lofty idea, but the encounter with an event, a person, which gives life a new horizon and a decisive direction."* —Pope Benedict XVI, *Deus Caritas Est* (1) 2006

*Photo Credit: The Wedding at Cana, Christ and the Virgin © Erich Lessing/Art Resource, NY*

3. What qualities might be exhibited by a couple who has Jesus at the center of their marriage? What clues would you look for?

_____

_____

## COUPLE'S DISCUSSION

**God in Your Daily Life**

| 0 | 1 | 2 | 3 | 4 | 5 | 6 | 7 | 8 | 9 | 10 |
|---|---|---|---|---|---|---|---|---|---|---|

1. On a scale of 1–10, how much do you bring God into your marital relationship and family life on a daily basis? (10 being "very often" and 1 being "We don't ever talk about God.")

_____

_____

2. What are some things you can do together as a couple to put God at the center of your marriage and your family life?

_____

_____

3. The video makes the point that having Jesus as the center of your marriage takes the pressure off both spouses because it frees them from having to worry about meeting one another's every need. What difference has that freedom made in your marriage—or what difference *would* it make?

_____

_____

"*The Eucharist draws us into Jesus' act of self-oblation. More than just statically receiving the incarnate Logos, we enter into the very dynamic of his self-giving.*" —Pope Benedict XVI, *Deus Caritas Est* 13

# CLOSING PRAYER

The following is an excerpt of Pope Francis from the homily of the Holy Mass for the conclusion of the Year of Faith, November 24, 2013:

*"Christ is the center of the history of humanity and also the center of the history of every individual. To him we can bring the joys and the hopes, the sorrows and troubles which are part of our lives. When Jesus is the center, light shines even amid the darkest times of our lives; he gives us hope…"*

**PRAYER OF ST. PATRICK**

Christ with me,
Christ before me,
Christ behind me,
Christ in me,
Christ beneath me,
Christ above me,
Christ on my right,
Christ on my left,
Christ when I lie down,
Christ when I sit down,
Christ when I arise,
Christ in the heart of every man who thinks of me,
Christ in the mouth of everyone who speaks of me,
Christ in every eye that sees me,
Christ in every ear that hears me.

## COUPLE'S ACTIVITY

Think about the number you gave yourself (on a scale of 1–10) when it comes to bringing Christ into your marital relationship and family life on a daily basis. In fact, you might want to write that number in a place where you'll see it often. Your goal is to increase that number by at least 1 in the coming week.

Think about the steps you can take to involve Christ more intimately and significantly in your marriage and family this week. In addition to obvious strategies such as attending Mass together, you might consider these ideas:

- Schedule a short time to pray together every morning or evening.
- Find a program at the parish to attend together (such as a Bible study, a retreat, or a lecture).
- Go out with another couple who shares your faith and priorities in life.
- Identify other priorities that keep Christ on the outside, and take steps to reduce their influence.

After a week of these and other strategic fixes, you should be able to say with confidence, "Our marriage and family life is more Christ-centered now than it was a week ago."

# *Your Journal Thoughts*

# SESSION 2

## A DEEPER UNITY

# SESSION 2

## A DEEPER UNITY

## INTRODUCTION

The rush of first love is like the taste of grape juice: exciting, bold, and slightly overpowering. Mature love, on the other hand, is like the taste of a fine wine: complex, flavorful, and far superior to grape juice. In order to enjoy a mature love, though, you must endure the "fermenting" process—the difficulties and challenges that God uses to bring out the best in you and your marriage.

You and your spouse have an adventure that you are called to share in Christ. That adventure flows into your love for your family, your friends, your church, and the world. When you have a big-picture perspective of your adventure, you can see where everything fits.

## OPENING PRAYER

***Pray together the following prayer:***

We thank you, O God, for the marital guidance found in your Word, for the timeless wisdom contained in these passages:

*"Do nothing from selfishness or conceit, but in humility count others better than yourselves. Let each of you look not only to his own interests, but also to the interests of others."* —Philippians 2:3-4

*"The Son of Man came not to be served but to serve, and to give his life as a ransom for many."* —Matthew 20:28

*"Be subject to one another out of reverence for Christ."* —Ephesians 5:21

Move in our midst today, Lord. Guide our efforts to deepen our marriages, as well as our relationship with you.

Amen.

*"Set me as a seal upon your heart, as a seal upon your arm; for love is strong as death, jealousy is cruel as the grave. Its flashes are flashes of fire, a most vehement flame. Many waters cannot quench love, neither can floods drown it. If a man offered for love all the wealth of his house, it would be utterly scorned."*
—Song of Solomon 8:6-7

# SMALL GROUP DISCUSSION

**1. What connection do you see between God's relationship with the Israelites and your relationship with your spouse?**

_____

_____

**2. Describe the difference between a "grape juice" love and a "fine wine" love.**

_____

_____

**3. If marriage is an adventure that couples are called to share in Christ, what's the best way to approach that adventure?**

_____

_____

**4. Agree or disagree: If you don't regularly experience conflict or challenge in your marriage, your relationship is not maturing at a healthy rate.**

_____

_____

# COUPLE'S DISCUSSION

**1. How do you and your spouse complement one another or balance each other out?**

_____

_____

**2. How does it change your outlook on your marriage to know that struggles and "wilderness experiences" are part of God's plan?**

_____

_____

**3. What are two challenges or situations that God has used to deepen your marriage?**

_____

*Photo Credit: Moses brings forth water from rock and manna from desert / Alfredo Dagli Orti / The Art Archive at Art Resource, NY*

- **How has your marriage stretched, grown, or matured as a result?**

_____

_____

- **How did your past challenges or situations prepare you for future challenges?**

_____

_____

> *"Two such as you with such a master speed*
> *Cannot be parted nor be swept away*
> *From one another once you are agreed*
> *That life is only life forevermore*
> *Together wing to wing and oar to oar"*
> —from "The Master Speed" by Robert Frost

## CLOSING PRAYER

Almighty God,

We praise you for the model of selfless, sacrificial love you demonstrated in your relationship with the Israelites. We thank you for the wilderness experiences that you use to deepen our relationships—for the challenges and dark times that ultimately produce maturity, appreciation, and fulfillment. Bless our efforts to understand those experiences, to survive and thrive in the midst of them.

Your Word tells us that we are fearfully and wonderfully made. We give thanks to you for the opportunity...

- to examine the crowning work of your creation in our spouse every day,
- to study the intricacies of your design, and
- to use our knowledge of that design to express love to our spouse in meaningful ways.

Guide us as we work to build a marriage that honors you and reflects your grace, now and for the rest of our lives.

We ask this through Christ our Lord. Amen.

## COUPLE'S ACTIVITY

Regardless of how long you've been married, you've probably become somewhat of an expert on your spouse's likes, dislikes, favorite foods, proudest moments, and biggest pet peeves. It's time to take inventory of what you know and put it to good use.

Job #1 is to create a bio sheet for your spouse. Use the chart on the next page, or create a file on your computer (or in a journal or notebook) devoted solely to personal information about your spouse. There need be no rhyme or reason to the information. You can simply list things you've learned about your spouse as they occur to you.

# BIO SHEET

Likes

Dislikes

Noteworthy
Accomplishments

Personal Highlights

Talents

Abilities

Favorite Songs

Favorite Movies

Favorite Restaurant

Favorite Snacks

Favorite Relaxation Spots

Other Relevant Bits
of Information

Once you have a workable bio, you can plan some highly personalized, highly meaningful surprises for your spouse. Using the information you've gathered over the course of your marriage, devise some effective—and unexpected—ways to demonstrate your love.

The video presenter gathered flower petals from the Holy Land and placed them in his wife's Bible. Here are a few other ideas, to get you thinking:

- Have your spouse's favorite lunch delivered to the office.
- Make a playlist of songs that have special meaning for your spouse.
- Put together a small photo album of pictures from various points in your relationship, each one with a caption that explains what you love about your spouse in that picture.

*Your Journal Thoughts*

# SESSION 3

## CONFLICT AND COMMUNICATION

# SESSION 3

## CONFLICT AND COMMUNICATION

### INTRODUCTION

Conflict in marital relationships often causes us to shift our focus from our spouse to the conflict itself. Instead of working together to battle the conflict, we battle each other. The most common areas of conflict are money, sex, children, work, household responsibilities, and our relationships with friends and family.

The cause of a conflict isn't always what it seems, though. In order to understand what's driving a conflict, you have to "lift the hood" of your marriage and look inside. Among the things that drive conflicts are fear, woundedness, insecurity, shame, and a lack of forgiveness. Once you discover what's driving your conflict, you can approach it together and it can actually become an occasion to grow even closer to your spouse.

### OPENING PRAYER

***Pray together the following prayer:***

In Proverbs 27:17, we read, "Iron sharpens iron, and one man sharpens another."

Almighty Father, the conflicts that we resolve in our marriage sharpen us and make us keener instruments of your grace and glory. Bless our efforts to understand conflict better, to work through our conflicts together with our spouse in order to strengthen and deepen our understanding of one another. We ask this through Christ our Lord.

Amen.

*"And whenever you stand praying, forgive, if you have anything against anyone; so that your Father also who is in heaven may forgive you your trespasses."*
—Mark 11:25

# SMALL GROUP DISCUSSION

**1. Of the top six areas of conflict—money, sexuality, children, work, household responsibilities, and family and friends—which one has caused you the least amount of trouble in your marriage? Explain.**

_____

_____

**• Which area of conflict has caused the most trouble?**

_____

_____

**2. What does it mean to "lift up the hood" on your relationship?**

_____

_____

**• Why might some people be reluctant to lift up the hood of their relationship?**

_____

_____

**3. What do you wish someone had told you about conflict before you got married?**

_____

_____

> *"The love of Christ can restore to spouses the joy of journeying together. This is what marriage is all about: man and woman walking together, wherein the husband helps his wife to become ever more a woman, and wherein the woman has the task of helping her husband to become ever more a man."*
> —Pope Francis, Homily on June 14, 2014

# COUPLE'S DISCUSSION

**1. How have your conflict-resolution skills developed over the course of your marriage?**

_____

**2. How much work do you have to do in refining your conflict-resolution skills?**

_____

_____

*Photo Credit: Young happy couple talking together sitting on a sofa © Valery Sidelnykov/Shutterstock.com*

*"In an epoch marked by hatred, selfishness, the desire for false happiness, by the decadence of customs, the absence of father and mother figures, instability in numerous young families, and by widespread frailty and hardship to which many young people fall prey, we look to you, Jesus in the Eucharist, with renewed hope."*
—St. John Paul II, Message to the young people of Rome and Lazio, March 15, 2005

## CLOSING PRAYER

*"We all know there is no such thing as the perfect family or a perfect husband or wife. I won't even mention a perfect mother-in-law... It's us who do exist, sinners. Jesus knows us well and he tells us a secret: Never let the day end without apologizing."*
—Pope Francis, to engaged couples on February 14, 2014

Our Father, who art in heaven, hallowed be thy name; thy kingdom come, thy will be done on earth as it is in heaven. Give us this day our daily bread; and forgive us our trespasses as we forgive those who trespass against us; and lead us not into temptation, but deliver us from evil.

Amen.

## COUPLE'S ACTIVITY

Set aside some time this week to create a "Geneva Convention" for your marriage. In international terms, the Geneva Conventions are protocols for the humane treatment of combatants during armed conflict. They are intended to prevent cruelty. That's your goal as well.

Conflict, if not worked through properly, can bring out the worst in people. Otherwise loving and caring spouses find themselves saying or doing things in the midst of heated conflict that would have seemed unimaginable to them in any other situation. In some cases, this may be attributed to a competitive nature run amok. The desire to "win" the conflict at any cost becomes irresistible. In other cases, it may be attributed to a traumatic (and perhaps even abusive) upbringing.

When conflict is worked through properly—when couples feel safe in "looking under the hood" together—it can produce profoundly positive results. Proverbs 27:17 compares it to iron sharpening iron. The key is to create a healthy dynamic in your relationship in which conflict can be discussed and worked through with no damage to your marriage. That's where this exercise comes in.

Choose a comfortable setting for your discussion, one that offers intimacy and privacy. Ideally you'll want to do this when there's no active conflict between you and your spouse. Otherwise your attempts to create your own Geneva Conventions may get caught up in the conflict.

This is the place for transparency and openness. Talk about the things that bother you when you argue with your spouse. Talk about the things that hurt your feelings or push your buttons. Talk about the sensitive topics and issues that should never be used as ammunition.

Draw up a list of resolutions based on your discussion. You may want to phrase them as promises. For example:

- I promise not to use the words "always" and "never" (as in "You always do this" or "You never do that") during a conflict. Instead, I will stick with specifics.
- I promise not to bring up past conflicts that have already been resolved.
- I promise not to raise my voice.
- I promise not to confront you about something until after I've prayed about it.
- I promise not to share the details of our conflict with other people.

**RESOLUTIONS**

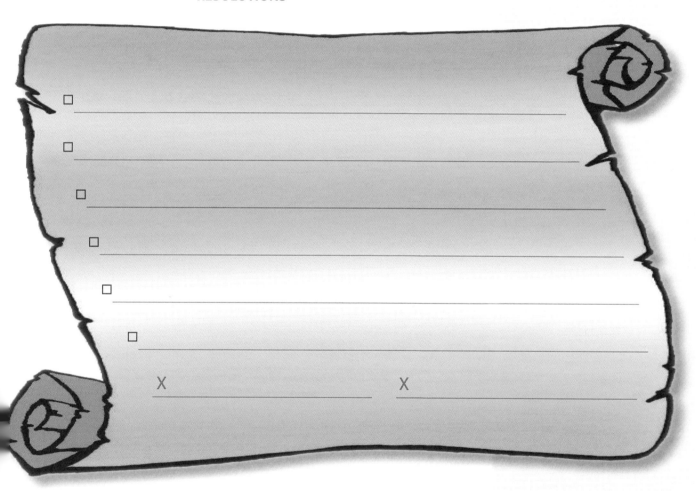

Sign the sheet together—not as a legally binding document, but as a sign of your good faith and your desire not to hurt one another in the midst of conflict.

# *Your Journal Thoughts*

_____

_____

_____

_____

_____

_____

_____

_____

_____

_____

_____

_____

_____

_____

_____

_____

_____

# SESSION 4

## BUILDING A THRIVING MARRIAGE

## BUILDING A THRIVING MARRIAGE

### INTRODUCTION

Marriage involves a specific set of tasks and responsibilities:

- We must be aware of ourselves.
- We must do the work that is required of us.
- We must find ways to be together with our spouse.
- We must pursue virtue.
- We must be patient with each other.

One thing that gets in the way of the work of marriage is woundedness. A wound is an experience of unlove. A wound causes pain, which causes fear, which leads to managing behaviors in an effort to avoid the pain. Woundedness must be met with an authentic experience of love—a blessing from God or another person. A blessing triggers feelings of being loved, which trigger gratitude and security, which trigger expressions of love.

### OPENING PRAYER

**Pray together the following prayer from the Second Vatican Council:**

We stand before you, Holy Spirit, gathered in your name. Come to us, remain with us, and enlighten our hearts. Give us light and strength to know your will, to make it our own, and to live it in our lives.

Guide us by your wisdom, support us by your power, for you are God, sharing the glory of Father and Son. Unite us to yourself in the bond of love, and keep us faithful to all that is true. You live and reign with the Father and the Son, one God, for ever and ever.

Amen.

*"Love is the prime gift. Whatever else is freely given to us becomes a gift only through love."*
—Anonymous by Catholic philosopher Josef Pieper, *Faith, Hope, Love*

# SMALL GROUP DISCUSSION

**1. What's the most impressive thing you've ever accomplished? Explain.**

_____

_____

**• Where does your marriage rank among your most impressive achievements? Explain.**

_____

_____

**2. Of the five things couples can do to pursue God's ideal for their relationship— be aware of yourself, do the work, be together, pursue virtue, and be patient— which one would you say is most difficult? Explain.**

_____

_____

**3. Describe a relationship you've seen struggle because of woundedness.**

_____

_____

*"May you be torches that burn in the middle of the world: where there is a night of unbelief, may the light of your faith cast a strong light; where there is the soot of hatred and despair, may the glow of your optimism and hope shine in; where there is the darkness of selfishness and violence, let the fire of your love burn bright."*
—St. John Paul II, Speech to Youth, Imola, Italy, May 9, 1986

# COUPLE'S DISCUSSION

**1. What would happen to your marriage if you became more aware of yourselves, did the work of marriage, made a point of being together more, pursued virtue more passionately, and learned to be more patient with each other? How good could you be together? What might be some of the results?**

_____

_____

**2. What impact has woundedness—that is, past experiences of "unlove"— had on your marriage?**

_____

_____

*Photo Credit: The Marriage of the virgin/Alfredo Dagli Orti/The Art Archive at Art Resource, NY*

## CLOSING PRAYER

*"The family finds in the plan of God the Creator and Redeemer not only its identity, what it is, but also its mission, what it can and should do....Each family finds within itself a summons that cannot be ignored and that specifies both its dignity and its responsibility. Family, become what you are."*

—St. John Paul II, *Familiaris Consortio* 17

**Pray together the following prayer:**

Go with us, Father, as we depart from here. Bless our efforts to build relationships that approach your ideal. Work in our hearts and in our minds to refine us and make us better instruments of your grace.

Amen.

*"It is risky to get married: it is risky! It is this egoism which threatens it, because we each have within us this possibility of a dual personality: the one that says, 'I am free, I want this ...' and the other which says, 'I, me, to me, with me, for me ....'"*
—Pope Francis, meeting with the young people of Umbria, October 4, 2013

## COUPLE'S ACTIVITY

Marriage is work—the most rewarding work we'll ever do. And when there's work to be done, one of the most helpful resources available to us is a to-do list. Set aside some time this week with your spouse in order to make a to-do list for your marriage. It could be your date-night activity!

Put some thought into the items you include on your list. Be specific. Don't settle for something vague like "Spend more time together"; instead, opt for something more specific like "Take a walk around the block together every evening after dinner."

*Couple having fun together © Kzenon/Shutterstock.com*

Depending on your circumstances, your list may include items such as…

- Schedule an appointment with a marriage counselor.
- Attend Mass together at 8:45 on Sunday.
- Go to Confession as a family on the 15th of every month.
- Volunteer for a ministry together.
- Plan this week's date night.

Compiling your list is Step 1. Scheduling it is Step 2. Pull out your planners and set a start date for each job on your list. Honor the times you set. Don't allow your marriage enrichment plans to be pre-empted. Give your relationship the priority it deserves.

## TO-DO LIST

**STEP 1: To Do**          **STEP 2: Scheduling**

# *Your Journal Thoughts*

_____

_____

_____

_____

_____

_____

_____

_____

_____

_____

_____

_____

_____

_____

_____

_____

_____

_____

# SESSION 5

## PROTECTING THE BOND

# SESSION 5

## PROTECTING THE BOND

### INTRODUCTION

God's ideal for marriage is that spouses continue to grow in love, grow in trust, grow in unity, and grow in closeness. That ideal, however, is not always our reality. Circumstances can prevent marital growth from occurring. Outside interests such as social media, career advancement, or the pursuit of a good time can rob a marital relationship of its potential. In this session, we'll discover how to protect the bond with help from the Holy Spirit.

### OPENING PRAYER

**Pray together the following prayer:**

Our Father in heaven, we ask for your blessing and help as we are gathered together. We pray for guidance in the matters of marriage and ask that you would clearly show us how to seek your ideal with a spirit of joy and enthusiasm. Give us the desire to find ways to excel in our relationships. Help us to work together and encourage each other to excellence. We ask that we would challenge each other to reach higher and further to be the best spouses—and vessels of your grace—that we can be.

Amen.

*"A good wife who can find? She is far more precious than jewels. The heart of her husband trusts in her, and he will have no lack of gain. She does him good, and not harm, all the days of her life."* —Proverbs 31:10-12

# SMALL GROUP DISCUSSION

**1. Explain how a married couple could go from the intimacy of their early days to living parallel lives, as described in the video. Have you seen this happen to any couple that you know?**

_____

_____

**2. Think about the description in the video of the family in the airport focusing on their individual phones and personal devices and not talking to one another. How close to home did this description hit? What are some of the challenges that you face in this area?**

_____

_____

**3. Gale Sayers called his book *I Am Third*. What are some of the challenges and drawbacks to making that title a reality in your own life?**

_____

_____

*"The human person is a special gift of the Creator and the Redeemer together. Indeed to be a bridegroom is to be aware of the gift. This awareness creates a new mentality, a new attitude, a new behavior when we see the gift in the works of creation and above all in people."*
—St. John Paul II, Speech to Youth of Civitavecchia, Italy, March 19, 1987

*Photo Credit: The Kiss/Cameraphoto Arte, Venice/Art Resource, NY*

## COUPLE'S DISCUSSION

**1. Create some visuals. In the first circle, make a pie chart that represents the way you spend your time during your waking hours. In the second circle, make a pie chart that represents the way your spouse spends his or her waking hours.**

**Use any or all of the following categories for your charts:**

- **Marriage/Family**
- **Career**
- **Church**
- **Personal Devices (Internet, social media, online games, messaging)**
- **Hanging Out with Friends**
- **Sports/Workouts**
- **Hobbies**
- **Watching TV**
- **Any other categories that apply**

**2. With input from your spouse, draw a pie chart that represents a reasonable, more marriage-friendly way of spending your waking hours.**

*Couple not talking to each other on a park bench © Ljupco Smokovski / Shutterstock.com*

*"If I speak in the tongues of men and of angels, but have not love, I am a noisy gong or a clanging cymbal. And if I have prophetic powers, and understand all mysteries and all knowledge, and if I have all faith, so as to remove mountains, but have not love, I am nothing. If I give away all I have, and if I deliver my body to be burned, but have not love, I gain nothing."* — 1 Corinthians 13:1-3

# CLOSING PRAYER

*Pray together the following prayer:*

Our Father, may everything we do begin with your inspiration,
continue with your help,
and reach perfection under your guidance.
With your loving care, guide us in our daily actions.
Help us to persevere with love and sincerity.
Teach us to judge wisely the things of earth
and to love the things of heaven.

Amen.

# COUPLE'S ACTIVITY

Based on the pie charts you filled out, identify the biggest current threat to your marriage and family time. Is it your careers? The time you spend hanging out with friends? The demands of your kids' sports?

_____

_____

After you identify the threat, ask yourselves two questions. The first question is, *How deeply has this threat infiltrated our marriage or family life?* Let's say, for example, that like many couples, you identify Personal Device Time—time spent in social media or online—as your biggest threat. Take a clear-eyed look at your daily habits and routines to see how big of a role Personal Device Time plays in them. Try to be as objective and honest as you can. Don't try to downplay or dismiss what you see. Don't grade yourselves on a curve or compare yourselves to other couples who seem to have it worse. Acknowledge the extent of the problem and take responsibility for it.

The second question is, *What steps can we take to battle it together (or as a family)?* Work up a strategy that is both effective and doable for your family. In the case of Personal Device Time, your strategy might look something like this:

1. Redefine terms. Many people claim that they have to be on their personal devices for their jobs or other reasons. Talk about what constitutes a "pressing" need. What is important? Does fantasy football count?

2. Identify motivations. Talk about the needs that drive your Personal Device Time, whether it's the fear of being excluded, the desire to be the first to know when something happens, or boredom and the need for constant stimulation.

3. Set limits. Agree to check your devices, say, once after dinner and once before bed. At all other times, they stay (turned off, or at least muted) in a location where they can't be easily accessed.

4. Hold one another accountable. You both have a vested interest in the strength and potential of your marriage. If you see something potentially harmful creeping into your relationship, you have the right—and the responsibility—to speak up. If you see one another falling back into old habits, you must say something.

_____

_____

Test your strategy to see how well it works, and then make any necessary tweaks or changes.

*Your Journal Thoughts*

_____

_____

_____

_____

_____

_____

_____

_____

# SESSION 6

## SEXUALITY AND AUTHENTIC LOVE

# SESSION 6

## SEXUALITY AND AUTHENTIC LOVE

## INTRODUCTION

Sexual intimacy, as intended by God, is unitive—a total gift of self, holding nothing back. It is more than just a biological union; it is a union of body, soul, and emotions. Sexual intimacy is also procreative. In the act of sex, spouses must always be open to the possibility of creating new human life. If the unitive or procreative dimension of sex is thwarted, genuine intimacy cannot occur. As we will see, the Church's teachings on sex are not a "no" to this or a "no" that, but actually a "yes" to authentic love—the love that we are all ultimately looking for.

## OPENING PRAYER

***Pray together the following prayer:***

Almighty God,

We gather today to answer the call of St. Paul to present our bodies as living sacrifices, holy and acceptable to you. Open our hearts to the wisdom of your plan for marital intimacy. Transform us by the renewal of our minds so that we may prove what is good and acceptable and perfect to you.

Amen.

*"I appeal to you therefore, brethren, by the mercies of God, to present your bodies as a living sacrifice, holy and acceptable to God, which is your spiritual worship. Do not be conformed to this world but be transformed by the renewal of your mind, that you may prove what is the will of God, what is good and acceptable and perfect."* —Romans 12:1-2

# SMALL GROUP DISCUSSION

**1. Catholic author Frank Sheed said, "Modern man practically never *thinks* about sex." Why is it important for us, as married couples, to *think about* the true meaning of sex?**

_____

_____

**2. God reveals to us the true meaning of sex. How is God's plan for sexuality good news—a "yes" to the fullest expression of intimacy and love?**

_____

_____

**3. What are some of the benefits a marital relationship might experience when the couple fully embraces God's plan for sex?**

_____

_____

> *"Seeing God's covenant with Israel in the image of exclusive and faithful married love, the prophets prepared the Chosen People's conscience for a deepened understanding of the unity and indissolubility of marriage…Tradition has always seen in the Song of Solomon a unique expression of human love, insofar as it is a reflection of God's love—a love 'strong as death' that 'many waters cannot quench.'"*
> —CCC 1611

# COUPLE'S DISCUSSION

**1. How has your sexual intimacy changed from your honeymoon until now?**

_____

_____

**2. Take an honest look at your sexual relationship and all that you have learned today about God's plan for sex. Then, have each of you identify one or two things that would help improve your sexual intimacy. (For example, better communication, increased vulnerability, deeper emotional bond, etc.)**

_____

*Photo Credit: Couple in Love © FCSCAFEINE/Shutterstock.com*

*"In destroying the power of giving life through contraception, a husband and wife are doing something to self. This turns attention to self, and so it destroys the gift of love in him or her."*

—Blessed Teresa of Calcutta,
Speech at the U.S. National Prayer Breakfast on February 3, 1984

## CLOSING PRAYER

***Pray together the Collect for Purity:***

O God, the King eternal, whose light divides the day from the night and turns the shadow of death into the morning: Drive far from us all wrong desires, incline our hearts to keep your law, and guide our feet into the way of peace; that, having done your will with cheerfulness during the day, we may, when night comes, rejoice to give you thanks; through Jesus Christ our Lord.

Amen.

## COUPLE'S ACTIVITY

Each of you should put some thought into this question: *What is the biggest obstacle to living out God's plan for sex and having genuine sexual intimacy in our relationship right now?* Don't reveal your answers to each other right away. Instead, set a time this week to sit down and share your thoughts.

Depending on your circumstances, you may say your biggest obstacle is…
- your attitude toward the possibility of having children
- having recourse to contraception or sterilization
- an interest in pornography that isn't as harmless as it seems
- an inability to track your fertility cycle

…or something else entirely. Be open and honest in your assessment.

If you and your spouse identify the same obstacle, your job is obvious: to work together to remove the obstacle. If, on the other hand, the two of you identify two very different obstacles, it may be an indication that you're further apart than you realize. Either way, you have the opportunity to brainstorm workable solutions for eliminating those obstacles from your relationship.

For example, to realign your attitude toward having children, you might talk about the concerns that make you reluctant and find workable solutions to them. To address the issue of pornography, you may need to discuss in detail the behaviors associated with it and plan strategies for counteracting them. To learn to track your fertility cycle more accurately, you may enroll in an NFP course through your local parish or diocese.

# *Your Journal Thoughts*

_____

_____

_____

_____

_____

_____

_____

_____

_____

_____

_____

_____

_____

_____

_____

_____

_____

_____

*Photo Credit: Red Roses © MorganStudio/Shutterstock.com*

What do I really believe?